Devdutt Pattanaik loves to write, illustrate and lecture on the relevance of mythology in modern times. He has, since 1996, written over forty books and 700 columns for adults and children. He believes that stories are like chocolate Eclairs: you chew on the outside — the story — till you get to the soft sweetness inside — the idea. To know more, visit www.devdutt.com.

THE BOYS WHO FOUGHT

The Mahabharata for Children

DEVDUTT PATTANAIK

Illustrations by the Author

PUFFIN BOOKS

An imprint of Penguin Random House

PUFFIN BOOKS

USA | Canada | UK | Ireland | Australia
New Zealand | India | South Africa | China

Puffin Books is part of the Penguin Random House group of companies
whose addresses can be found at global.penguinrandomhouse.com

Published by Penguin Random House India Pvt. Ltd
7th Floor, Infinity Tower C, DLF Cyber City,
Gurgaon 122 002, Haryana, India

First published in Puffin Books by Penguin Random House India 2017

10 9 8 7 6 5 4 3 2 1

ISBN 9780143441618

For sale in the Indian Subcontinent only

Designed by Dhaivat Chhaya (Special Effects)
Typeset in Book Antiqua by Special Effects, Mumbai
Printed at Thomson Press India Ltd, New Delhi

www.penguin.co.in

For those who can fight without hating

Within infinite myths lies an eternal truth
Who knows it all?
Varuna has but a thousand eyes
Indra, a hundred
You and I, only two.

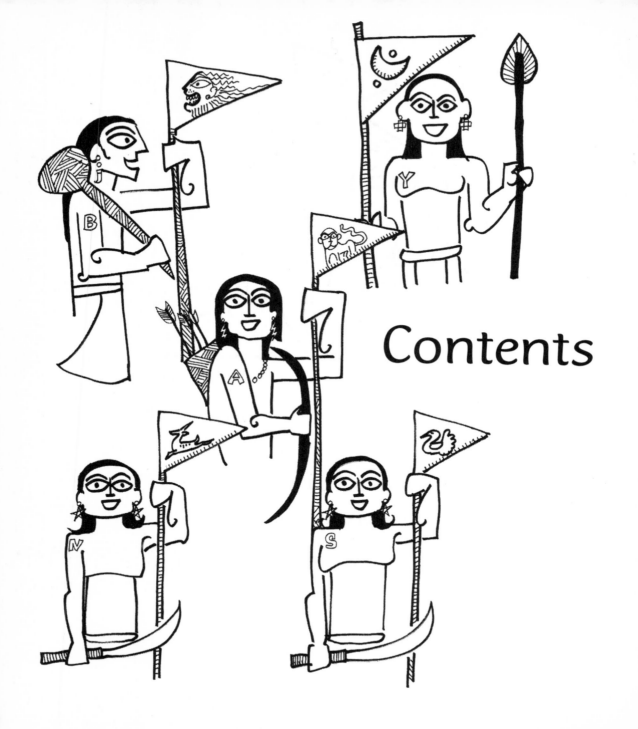

Contents

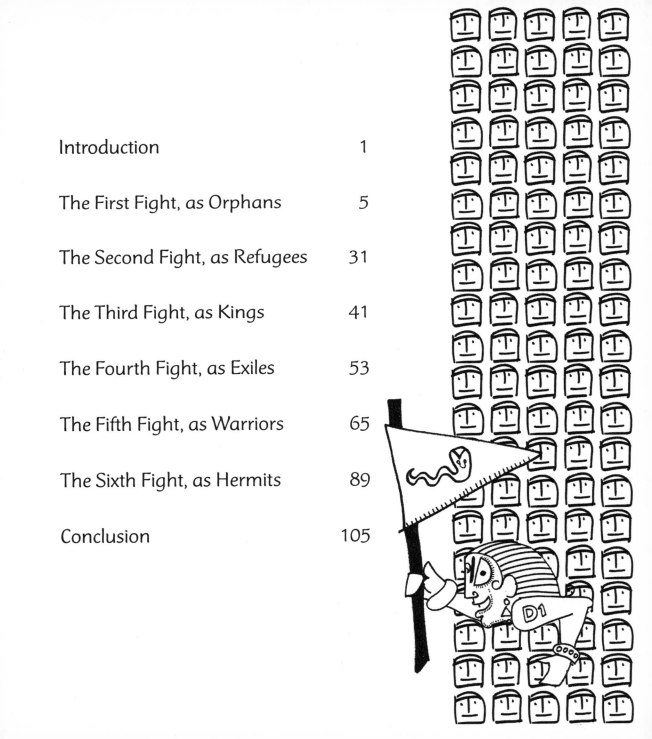

Introduction
A Very Long Epic

Once upon a time, there was a man called Vyasa. His father was a sage. His mother was a fisherwoman. He was born on a river island, and had a dark complexion.

Vyasa grew up watching animals fight. Then he saw humans fight. And he wondered, what was the difference?

In the forest, the mighty eat the meek. In human society, the mighty can take care of the meek.
This is dharma, realized Vyasa. It creates a decent human society.

Vyasa is also famous for organizing the Vedas, the oldest collection of Hindu hymns, so he is called Veda Vyasa.

Inspired, Vyasa wrote an incredible story in 1,00,000 verses, split into eighteen chapters, about the fight between a hundred brothers and their five cousins.

Ganesha, who has the head of an elephant, wrote down Vyasa's story, which became renowned as the Mahabharata, the great Indian epic, for Bharata is another name for India.

Others called it Bharata Kavya, the song of the Bharatas,

The Mahabharata has eighteen chapters and tells the story of eighteen armies who fought over eighteen days.

Events narrated in the Mahabharata may have actually taken place nearly 3000 years ago in the region around present-day Delhi. But the original Sanskrit epic reached its final form about 2000 years ago. Versions of this epic retold in regional languages, such as Telugu, Odia and Hindi, are less than 1000 years old.

for the hundred brothers and their five cousins belonged to the Bharata clan, also known as the Kuru clan, which once ruled over India.

Some people called the story Vijaya, the story of victory, for it describes how the Pandava five, with just seven armies, defeated the Kaurava hundred, with eleven armies, in an eighteen-day-long war.

Vyasa, however, insisted that his epic should be called Jaya, a victory in which no one was defeated. For, in the story, Krishna of the Yadu clan, cousin to both the Pandavas and the Kauravas, reveals a different kind of fight—a greater fight that takes place before weapons are raised on the battlefield, a fight of thoughts and emotions that arises inside our minds and hearts.

When you can fight for the meek without hating the mighty, you follow dharma.

The story of the grown-up Krishna is told in the Mahabharata. The story of the young Krishna is told in the Harivamsa, which is 1500 years old. Even later, the Bhagavatam or Bhagavata Purana was composed, in which Krishna is described as a form of Vishnu, the caretaker of the world.

A Very Long Epic

The First Fight, as Orphans

Pandu of the Kuru clan was pale as the moon. He was also king of Hastinapur. One day, he went to the forest to hunt deer. Unfortunately, though, he shot a sage and his wife, mistaking them for gazelles. To atone for this crime, Pandu decided to stay in the forest as a hermit.

Pandu had two wives, Kunti and Madri.
They left the palace to join him in the forest.

Your elder brother, Dhritarashtra, blind since birth, is now king in your place.

His wife, Gandhari, blindfolded since marriage, is now pregnant with his child.

I was once king and had two happy wives. Now I am cursed, neither king to my people nor husband who can give children to his wives.

The Boys Who Fought

It was then that Kunti told Pandu all was not lost. She had a mantra, a sacred formula, by which they could call on the gods to grant them children.

From Yama, the god of death and fairness, Kunti got the honest **Yudhishtira**.

From Vayu, the god of wind, Kunti got the mighty **Bhima**.

From Indra, the god of the sky and rain, Kunti got the talented **Arjuna**.

From the Ashwins, the horse-loving twin gods, Madri got twin sons, the handsome **Nakula** and the knowledgeable **Sahadeva**.

Pandu, his two wives and their five children lived happily in the forest for many years. Then one day Pandu died, and so did Madri. Kunti was left all alone to take care of the Pandavas.

The Boys Who Fought

The hermits in the forest told Kunti to go back to Pandu's house.

The forest is no place for children. There is the constant threat of wild animals eating them. And there is not enough food either, for rakshasas are sure to steal yours.

Go to your husband's house. Let their uncle, Dhritarashtra, and his uncle, Bhishma, take care of them.

The house of Pandu surely belongs to the Pandavas.

So Kunti took her children to Hastinapur, where the five Pandava brothers met their father's vast family.

Bhishma, the Pandavas' grand-uncle, gave up the throne and did not marry, so that his father, Shantanu, could marry Satyavati, who wanted her children and their children to be kings.

Dhritarashtra, Pandu's elder brother, was not made king initially because he was blind. (Vedic kings had to be unblemished.)

Gandhari, Dhritarashtra's wife, wore a blindfold to share her husband's blindness.

Vidura, adviser to the Kuru king, was treated like a younger brother, though his mother was a maid.

Kripa was the royal tutor.

The Boys Who Fought

The Pandavas learnt that they came from an illustrious family, the Kuru-kula, also known as the Bharatas or the Chandra-vamsa.

Family Tree

11

The brothers were soon introduced to their hundred cousins — the Kauravas. They also met their Kaurava sister, Dusshala.

I am the only girl in a house of a hundred brothers and five cousins.

How can they be my cousins? They look poor.

They don't look happy to see us.

Gandhari had given birth to a ball of flesh. A sage had cut it into a hundred pieces and put them into separate pots. From a hundred pots had come a hundred sons. And from an extra pot had been born a daughter. Duryodhana, the eldest, was born on the same day as Bhima.

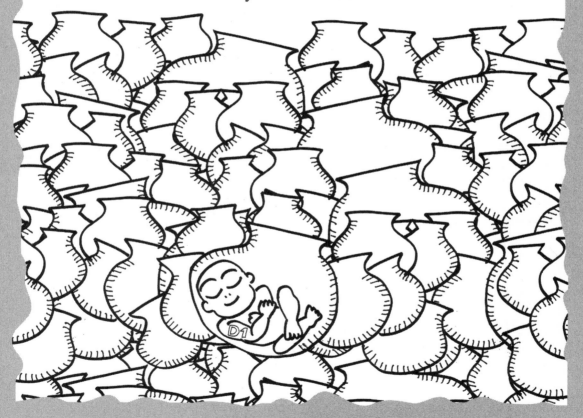

Kripa realized that the hundred Kauravas hated the five Pandavas.

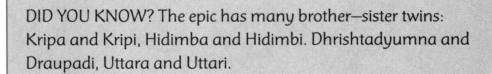

DID YOU KNOW? The epic has many brother—sister twins: Kripa and Kripi, Hidimba and Hidimbi. Dhrishtadyumna and Draupadi, Uttara and Uttari.

Drona agreed to help Kripa and teach the art of warfare to the Kuru princes. But he had one condition.

The First Fight, as Orphans

So it came to pass that the hundred Kauravas and the five Pandavas became students in Drona's school.

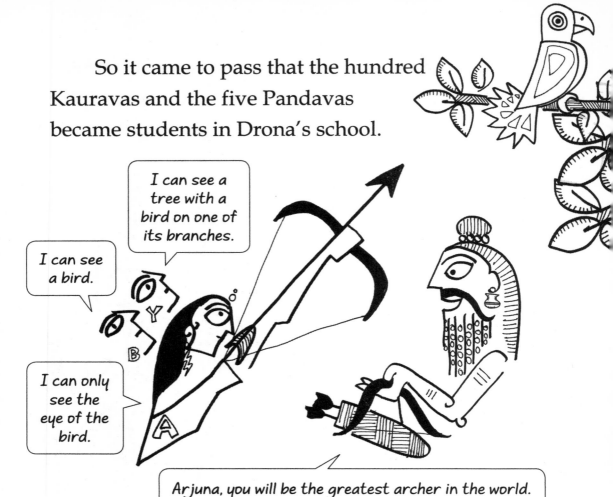

It was clear right from the start that the five Pandava brothers were stronger, smarter and more skilled than all the hundred Kauravas put together.

The Boys Who Fought

The talent of Arjuna and the strength of Bhima made Duryodhana extremely nervous. He turned to the only man he could trust—his mother's brother, Shakuni.

On Shakuni's advice, Duryodhana invited Bhima over for a meal. Bhima loved eating, and did not realize he was being served poisoned food. And when, overpowered by the venom, Bhima fainted, the Kauravas tied his hands and feet and threw him in the river. He would have surely drowned had the nagas not rushed to his rescue and brought him back to Hastinapur, much to Duryodhana's disappointment.

Nagas are serpent-like creatures who live under the earth, in the forests and in the waters. They have access to gems that can cure all ailments and even bring the dead back to life.

The Boys Who Fought

Nobody believed Bhima when he accused Duryodhana of trying to kill him. So Bhima spent all his free time chasing and beating up the Kauravas. They would climb trees to escape Bhima's wrath but he would shake the tree vigorously, causing them to fall like fruit.

One day, the five Pandavas met Ekalavya, a tribal boy who claimed to be Drona's student as well. He was a brilliant archer, who could shoot arrows into a dog's mouth to stop it from barking without even killing it.

The Boys Who Fought

In many tribal communities, Ekalavya is a hero. Several years later, Arjuna is defeated by a tribal during a boar hunt and made to realize that being a prince does not make him special.

As the years passed, Drona's 105 royal students became experts at wielding their weapons of choice: the spear for Yudhishtira, the mace for Bhima, the bow for Arjuna and the sword for Nakula and Sahadeva. Duryodhana too learnt to command the mace. Drona's son, Ashwatthama, also learnt archery from his father. But while Duryodhana equalled Bhima in mace warfare, Ashwatthama was no match for Arjuna in archery.

When their education was complete, each one was given a flag bearing their unique symbol: the moon for Yudhishtira, the lion for Bhima, the monkey for Arjuna, the antelope for Nakula and the swan for Sahadeva. Perhaps it reflected their personality. The symbol on Duryodhana's flag was a snake, the cobra.

Drona organized a tournament to show the world how well he had trained the Kuru princes. The Pandavas were clearly better than the Kauravas, and Arjuna was, without doubt, the greatest archer. Everyone cheered them on.

But then a young boy with radiant armour and shiny earrings appeared from the crowds, picked up the bow and proved that he was a far better archer, eclipsing Arjuna's glory. Who was he?

The Boys Who Fought

Drona refused to change the rules, and so did Bhishma. The Pandavas were happy. The Kauravas were furious.

The First Fight, as Orphans

Kunti, mother of the Pandavas, had a secret. Before her marriage to Pandu, she had used a mantra and secured a son from Surya, the sun-god. But she had abandoned him to a river's whim. This was Karna, found and raised by charioteers.

Oh! Karna is my abandoned son.

Drona, teacher of the Pandavas, also had a secret.

A long time ago, I was very poor—so poor that I could not give my son, Ashwatthama, milk to drink. So I asked my childhood friend Drupada, king of Panchala, for a cow. But he insulted me.

How can you claim to be a friend? When we were children, we were equal. But now I am a king, and you are a beggar. Only equals can be friends.

One day, I will be your equal. Then I will force you to be my friend.

I have trained the Kuru princes in the art of warfare to ask them for half your kingdom as tuition fee.

Fully trained in the crafts of war, the Kauravas and the Pandavas had to now repay Drona for his teachings. And so they attacked the kingdom of Panchala, defeated King Drupada and laid claim to one half of his kingdom, giving it to their teacher. Drona was ecstatic; he had got his tuition fee and his revenge.

The Boys Who Fought

The city of Hastinapur rejoiced on learning of the Kurus' triumph over the king of Panchala. They hoped and prayed that the victory had forged a friendship between the hundred sons of Dhritarashtra and the five sons of Pandu.

To maintain peace, Dhritarashtra asked his sons to build a palace for their cousins. It was a beautiful mansion, worthy of the Pandavas. It made the five orphans very happy. For the first time, they felt loved in their uncle's kingdom.

But that very night, when everyone was asleep, the palace caught fire. For it was made of wax!

When the fire died down, there was no trace of the Pandavas or their mother. Everyone assumed they were dead, burnt to ashes. Vidura wept. Bhishma wept. Gandhari wept. Dhritarashtra wept. Dusshala wept. But Duryodhana and Shakuni laughed. Their plan had worked.

The Boys Who Fought

The Second Fight, as Refugees

Through an underground tunnel, the Pandavas had escaped to the forest.

The Pandavas did not tell people who they were. They pretended to be five orphan children with their widowed mother. They never stayed in one place for long. They walked all day and spent only their nights in villages.

Life was a struggle. In the forest, you have to compete with other animals for food and keep watch for predators who think you are food. Sometimes, when everyone would be too tired to walk to the next village, Bhima would pick up his mother and his brothers and carry them on his shoulders so that they could reach their destination.

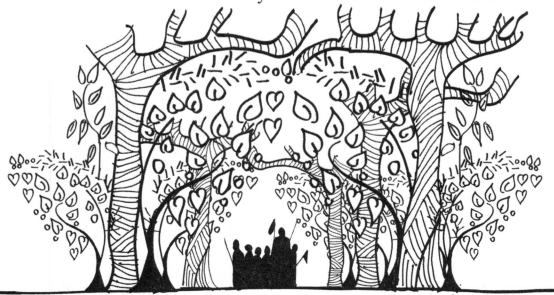

Once, the Pandavas saw their hosts for the night loading a cart with food and bidding a tearful farewell to their son.

33

Since the villagers had taken care of them,
Kunti offered to send one of her sons into the forest
instead — Bhima. The villagers could not believe
their luck, and thanked Kunti for her generosity and
sacrifice. Bhima chuckled, for this was Kunti's way
of ensuring he had a lot to eat even as he took care
of the rakshasa problem once and for all. Bhima rode
the cart to the forest, ate all the food himself and
when Baka attacked him, fought the rakshasa and
killed him.

He then proceeded to kill
many other rakshasas
who troubled the local
villagers, including
the terrible Hidimba.

The Boys Who Fought

To make peace, Hidimbi, sister of the rakshasa
Hidimba, asked Bhima to be her husband.
Hidimbi looked after Bhima and his family. She bore
Bhima a son, the mighty Ghatotkacha, and promised
to bring harmony between the people who lived in
the villages and those who lived in the forest.

Hidimbi or Hadimba Devi is worshipped as a forest goddess in
Himachal Pradesh.

Many months later, the Pandavas learnt that Drupada was organizing an archery contest in Panchala, and the winner would marry his daughter, Draupadi. What they did not know was the purpose of Draupadi's birth.

I made offerings to a holy fire and asked the gods for two favours.

A son who will kill Drona, teacher of the Kuru princes.

A daughter who will divide the Kuru kingdom as the Kuru princes divided the Panchala kingdom.

The gods granted Drupada the children he desired: a son called Dhrishtadyumna and a beautiful daughter called Draupadi. They were born from the fire not as children, but all grown up.

The Boys Who Fought

Karna was not allowed to participate in the archery contest as he was a charioteer's son. He never forgave Draupadi for it. But the Pandavas attended the contest in Panchala.

At the competition, archers were asked to pierce the eye of a fish, rotating along a wheel hanging from the ceiling, while only looking at its reflection in a pool below. Arjuna won easily.

The Boys Who Fought

At the wedding of Draupadi and the Pandavas, the Pandavas met Krishna for the first time.

I am the son of Vasudeva, the Yadava.

I am Kunti, Vasudeva's sister.

Then, Krishna, you are our cousin.

DID YOU NOTICE? Krishna's father, Vasudeva, is the Pandavas' *mama* (maternal uncle), just as Shakuni is the Kauravas' *mama*.

The Pandavas were no longer afraid and did not need to hide in the forest. So, with Draupadi, they presented themselves in front of their uncle in Hastinapur.

The Boys Who Fought

The Third Fight, as Kings

The Kuru elders were embarrassed and full of guilt when they saw the Pandavas and their mother emerge from the forest, accompanied by Draupadi and Krishna. To make amends, restore peace and avoid scandal, the kingdom was divided in two.

The developed half, with Hastinapur, for the Kauravas

The undeveloped half, the forest of Khandava, for the Pandavas

Many people do not like to read the Mahabharata at home as it speaks of the division of family property. They prefer the Ramayana as it speaks of keeping the family property united.

The forest that once gave refuge to the Pandavas was now their property. They could do anything with it.

> I want to build a city here.

> Then you have to burn this forest down.

> Is there no other way?

> No.

The forest is wild land where man has no control.
The field is domesticated land where man is in control.

The Boys Who Fought

And so the forest was set afire and given as offering to Agni, the fire-god. The flames destroyed the trees and all the birds and beasts that lived in the forest.

We nagas who survived will take revenge on the Pandavas.

I, Maya, a resident of the forest who was spared, will build a city for the Pandavas.

When the fire died down, Maya built a
magnificent palace for the Pandavas. They called it
Indraprastha. Here Draupadi was the queen, and she
lived with her five husbands. Soon, she gave birth to
five children, one son by each husband. They were
called the Upa-Pandavas.

The Boys Who Fought

Shortly after, Arjuna went on a pilgrimage and during this journey, he married three women, each of whom bore him a son.

In Tamil retellings of the Mahabharata, Arjuna marries many more women, including Ayli, a warrior woman.

Meanwhile, Yudhishtira was not content with just being owner of Indraprastha. He wanted to be crowned its king.

For that you have to earn the respect of all the kings of Bharata.

For that you have to defeat Jarasandha of Magadha, whom all kings fear.

For that you have to get Bhima to challenge Jarasandha to a wrestling match, for you don't have an army that can defeat his on a battlefield.

Every Pandava was an Indra, ruler of paradise, reborn. Draupadi was Sachi, their queen, reborn.

The Boys Who Fought

All went as planned. Jarasandha accepted
Bhima's challenge to a wrestling match. During the
duel, Bhima split Jarasandha's body into two and
threw each half on opposite sides, as advised by
Krishna. This was the only way to kill the king
of Magadha.

My two mothers ate one
half of a magic mango each,
and so each one gave birth
to half my body.

A rakshasa woman called
Jara stitched these two
halves together and gave
me life, which is why I am
called Jarasandha.

DID YOU KNOW? In the Mahabharata of the Jain
community, the great battle is between Krishna and
Jarasandha. The Pandavas support Krishna while the
Kauravas support Jarasandha.

News of Bhima killing Jarasandha impressed the kings of Bharata and they all came to Yudhishtira's coronation. The Kauravas came too. Seeing the success of their cousins, they grew very jealous.

Especially Duryodhana, who, while exploring the spectacular palace of the Pandavas, fell into a pool of water, mistaking it for solid ground. Draupadi, who witnessed this, burst out laughing. Duryodhana's jealousy quickly turned into anger.

Duryodhana then hatched a plot with Shakuni to snatch from the Pandavas all that they had acquired. The Kauravas invited the Pandavas to a gambling match. What the Pandavas did not know was that this was a trick to make Yudhishtira wager and lose everything they owned.

Yudhishtira loves to gamble.

But he is a bad board game player.

Indians invented many board games, like snakes and ladders as well as chess. These games were used for gambling. Stories like the Mahabharata warn of the dangers of gambling.

To humiliate the Pandavas even more, the Kauravas dragged Draupadi to the gambling hall and tried to publicly disrobe her.

This act disgusted even the gods, and a miracle occurred. Every time the Kauravas pulled away Draupadi's sari, new cloth appeared from thin air and draped itself around her body. Sari after sari appeared, until the frightened Kauravas stopped.

Realizing the gods were angry, Dhritarashtra begged Draupadi to forgive his stupid sons and leave the gambling hall in peace. She agreed.

But then the cunning Kauravas tricked the Pandavas into playing one more game. Once again, Yudhishtira agreed. Once again, he lost.

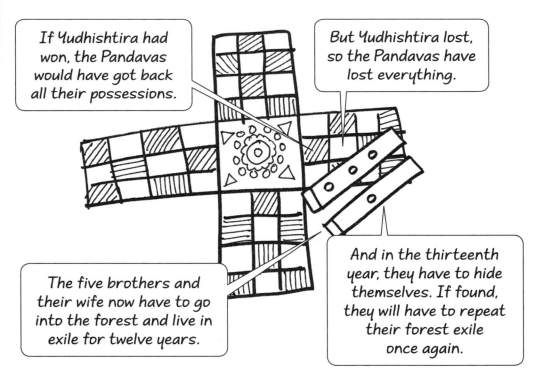

If Yudhishtira had won, the Pandavas would have got back all their possessions.

But Yudhishtira lost, so the Pandavas have lost everything.

The five brothers and their wife now have to go into the forest and live in exile for twelve years.

And in the thirteenth year, they have to hide themselves. If found, they will have to repeat their forest exile once again.

The Fourth Fight, as Exiles

Having lost everything at the gambling match, their wealth as well as their dignity, the Pandavas were now forced to live in the forest.

Krishna met the Pandavas in the forest, comforted them and promised to take care of their children while they were away. The Pandavas wanted to go to war against the Kauravas immediately, but Krishna advised them to keep their word and fulfil the conditions of the gambling match.

Let the forest teach you dharma. Travel across Bharata to all the pilgrimage spots, atop the mountains and where the rivers meet. Talk to sages. Let them tell you stories of great kings.

While the Pandavas were gambling away their kingdom and their freedom, Krishna had been busy defending his city, Dwaraka, against attacks by friends of Jarasandha.

The Boys Who Fought

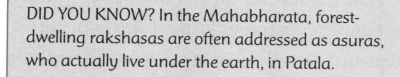

DID YOU KNOW? In the Mahabharata, forest-dwelling rakshasas are often addressed as asuras, who actually live under the earth, in Patala.

In the forest, the Pandavas were attacked by many rakshasas, like Kirmira and Jata. But Bhima defeated them all.

They also met many sages, like Markandeya, who told them many stories, including that of Sita and Ram, and discussed many philosophies. The Pandavas lived in caves, and travelled to several pilgrimage spots.

The Fourth Fight, as Exiles

In the forest, Arjuna once shot a wild boar.
But another hunter claimed the boar too.
Arjuna insisted the boar was his by right because he
was a prince. The hunter disagreed and challenged
Arjuna to fight for it. In the duel, Arjuna faced a
humiliating defeat. The hunter was none other than
Shiva. He taught Arjuna that a king must be generous.

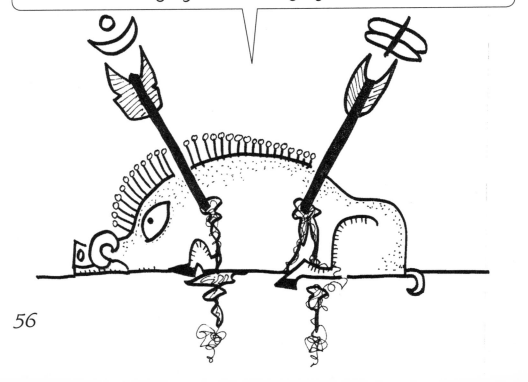

In the forest, there are no princes. No one is entitled to anything.
The hunt belongs to the strongest. For humans to accept the truth
of the jungle when in the jungle is dharma.

In the forest, Bhima walked straight, expecting all animals to move aside to make way for him. But an old monkey refused to move and asked Bhima to kick his tail away. Bhima realized that this monkey's tail was so heavy that he couldn't push it away even when he used all his strength. The monkey then revealed himself to be Hanuman. He taught Bhima that a king must be kind and humble.

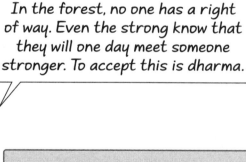

In the forest, no one has a right of way. Even the strong know that they will one day meet someone stronger. To accept this is dharma.

DID YOU NOTICE? Hanuman, a key character in the epic Ramayana, is also present in the epic Mahabharata.

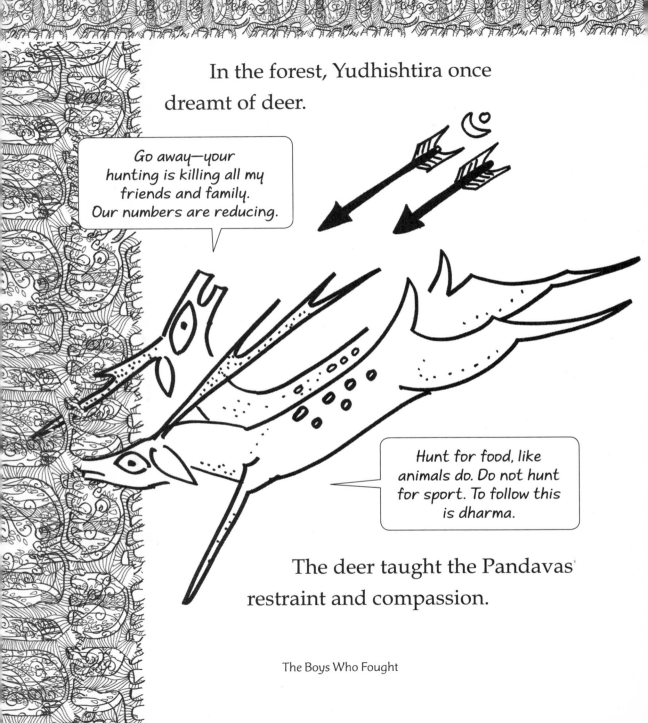

In the forest, Yudhishtira once dreamt of deer.

The deer taught the Pandavas restraint and compassion.

The Boys Who Fought

In the forest, Yudhishtira's brothers died when they drank water from a lake without answering a heron's questions.

But Yudhishtira did not drink until he had answered the heron's questions. His answers pleased the bird, for they showed Yudhishtira had understood dharma. But would Yudhishtira pass a test?

Select any one brother you want to live.

I choose Nakula.

Why not mighty Bhima or the great archer Arjuna?

My father had two wives, Kunti and Madri. I, a son of Kunti, am alive. Surely Nakula, a son of Madri, also deserves to live.

60

During the gambling match, Yudhishtira had gambled Nakula first, indicating he saw them as half-brothers, not brothers by blood. Exclusion is adharma.

By giving Nakula his life back, Yudhishtira shows he loves Madri's sons as much as he loves Kunti's sons. Inclusion is dharma.

In the Ramayana, Ram travels south during his forest exile. In the Mahabharata, the Pandavas travel mostly north, towards the Himalayas. However, there are caves and waterfalls across India that are believed to have been the residence of the Pandavas during their exile.

Yudhishtira is now ready to be king.

Yudhishtira became the king's gambling companion.

Bhima became the cook.

In the final year of exile, when they had to hide themselves from the world, the Pandavas went to the kingdom of Matsya, disguised themselves as servants and served in the palace of King Virata. They kept their identities secret, for if anyone recognized them, they would be forced to go back to the forest for another twelve years.

Arjuna became a transgender dance teacher.

Here, the Pandavas' whole world turned upside down. They were no longer the masters. They were no longer royal. No one treated them with respect. They were continuously humiliated. They saw how the rich mistreat the poor, how the powerful abuse the powerless, how employers exploit their employees. And so they learnt more in exile than they had as students of Drona.

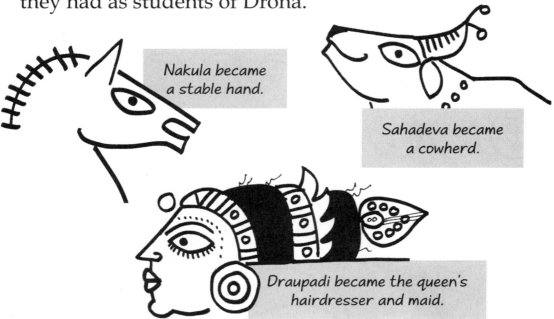

Nakula became a stable hand.

Sahadeva became a cowherd.

Draupadi became the queen's hairdresser and maid.

But one night, Virata's powerful brother-in-law, Kichaka, tried to misbehave with Draupadi. So Bhima attacked and killed him. News of Kichaka's death spread far and wide, as far as Hastinapur.

The Fifth Fight, as Warriors

The Kauravas were delighted at having located the Pandavas before the thirteenth year was over.

Unfortunately, their joy was short-lived. Bhishma said that the Kauravas' calculation was faulty by a year. They had not considered the extra month that needs to be added to a year every three years. So technically, the Pandavas had actually been in exile for more than thirteen years.

DID YOU NOTICE? Different societies use different calendars. Man-made calendars having twelve months need to be constantly modified to match the natural cycle of seasons. And so the modern calendar has some months with thirty days and some with thirty-one days. February sometimes has twenty-eight days and at other times, twenty-nine.

Drupada sent a messenger to the Kauravas on behalf of his sons-in-law, demanding that they keep their end of the bargain and return Pandava territory to the Pandavas. The Kauravas refused.

Then the Kauravas sent Sanjay, Dhritarashtra's charioteer, to tell the Pandavas not to return from their exile for the sake of peace. The Pandavas refused.

Then Krishna went to Hastinapur to reach a compromise. 'Don't give them everything. Just five villages,' said Krishna. The Kauravas refused. Instead they insulted the Pandavas for behaving like beggars.

It was clear that there would be no compromise nor peace. War had to be declared; sides had to be picked.

Shalya, the king of Madra, was tricked into fighting for the Kauravas, instead of supporting his nephews, Nakula and Sahadeva.

Krishna's elder brother, Balarama, who had taught advanced mace warfare techniques to both Bhima and Duryodhana, fought for neither the Kauravas nor the Pandavas.

Krishna supported both the Pandavas and the Kauravas: the Kauravas took his army while the Pandavas accepted him as Arjuna's charioteer.

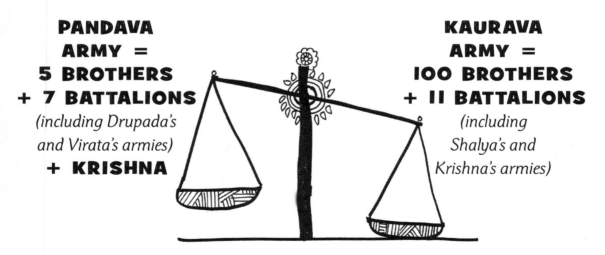

PANDAVA ARMY = 5 BROTHERS + 7 BATTALIONS
(including Drupada's and Virata's armies)
+ KRISHNA

KAURAVA ARMY = 100 BROTHERS + 11 BATTALIONS
(including Shalya's and Krishna's armies)

Bhishma led the Kaurava battalions while
Dhrishtadyumna led the Pandava battalions.
At Kuru-kshetra, the two armies met.

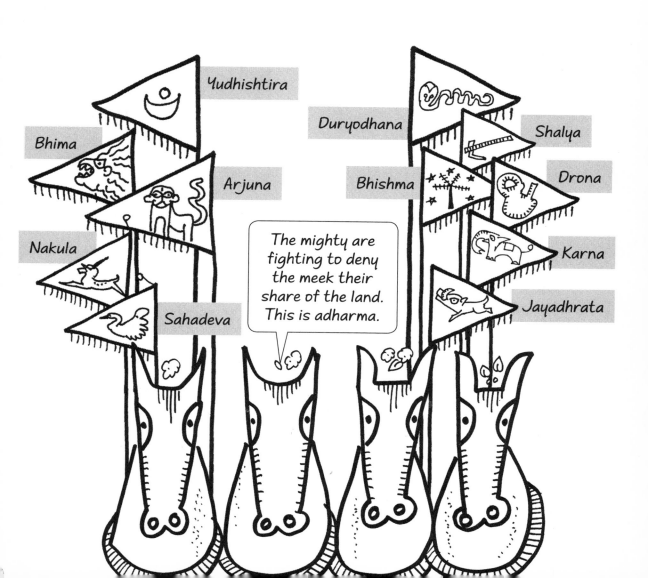

When Arjuna looked at either army, he realized that on both sides were his uncles and cousins and nephews.

GiTA

How can I fight my family? This is wrong.

DID YOU KNOW? Krishna's discourse to Arjuna is called the Bhagavad Gita. It has eighteen chapters and 700 verses. It contains Vedic wisdom.

The Gita was translated into Marathi from the original Sanskrit by Dnyaneshwar around 700 years ago, so that Krishna's words could reach the common man. Charles Wilkins translated the Gita into English over 200 years ago. There are nearly 3000 translations of the Gita today and in around fifty languages.

Enlightened by Krishna's words, Arjuna raised his conch-shell trumpet and declared war. A brutal battle followed, with arrows being released from every direction. The clanging of swords and the crashing of clubs filled the air, as did the screams of humans and the cries of horses and elephants.

Every warrior had a conch-shell trumpet, which was given a special name. Arjuna's conch-shell trumpet was called Devdutt, while Krishna's was called Panchajanya.

The Boys Who Fought

Hands were hacked off, stomachs ripped open, eyes gouged out. Every day, this began at dawn and ended at dusk, when the soldiers retired to their camps to nurse their injured bodies.

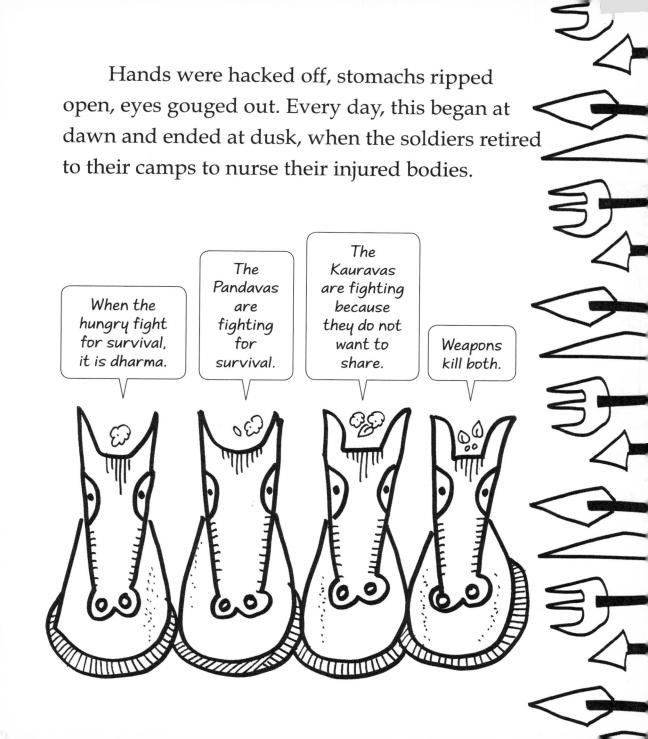

For nine days, the battle continued without either side winning. Both were equally strong. The Pandavas were confused.

To win, we have to kill Bhishma.

But he is immortal. He can choose the time of his death—a boon given by his father.

We have to immobilize Bhishma then.

Impossible! As long as he carries a bow, he cannot be defeated. He will not lower the bow before any man.

Then let us get a woman on to the battlefield.

Women are not allowed on the battlefield.

How about half a woman? Draupadi's elder brother Shikhandi was born with a woman's body and now has a man's body.

The Boys Who Fought

In my last life, I was Amba, princess of Kashi, who had sworn to kill Bhishma for ruining my life. Since I could not kill him in that life, I have been reborn as Shikhandi.

Bhishma refuses to fight me as he thinks I am a woman. He refuses to see that I am a man. He causes his own death by refusing to respect me.

With Shikhandi riding on a chariot before him, Arjuna attacked Bhishma. Bhishma refused to raise his bow against Shikhandi and so was easily toppled from his chariot. He could not be killed, so Krishna told Arjuna to pin the old man to the ground with his arrows.

After Bhishma's defeat, Drona became commander of the Kaurava army.

Drona was a ruthless warrior. Though a teacher, he broke all the rules of warfare. He created the Chakra-vyuha, a battle formation aimed at entrapping the Pandavas. But thanks to the efforts of Abhimanyu, the Pandavas escaped. Abhimanyu, however, got trapped.

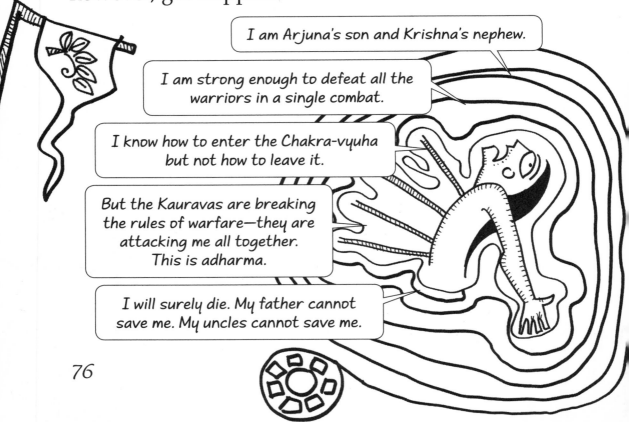

I am Arjuna's son and Krishna's nephew.

I am strong enough to defeat all the warriors in a single combat.

I know how to enter the Chakra-vyuha but not how to leave it.

But the Kauravas are breaking the rules of warfare—they are attacking me all together. This is adharma.

I will surely die. My father cannot save me. My uncles cannot save me.

Arjuna learnt how the Kauravas had killed Abhimanyu unfairly.

The Pandavas told him how Jayadhrata had stopped them from re-entering the Chakra-vyuha and saving their nephew. So Arjuna took an oath that he would kill Jayadhrata before sunset, saying, 'If I fail, I will kill myself.'

On learning this, the Kauravas did everything in their might to protect Jayadhrata until sunset. So Krishna used his powers and created the illusion that the sun had set.

In the darkness, as the Kauravas cheered in triumph, Krishna asked Arjuna to shoot an arrow in the direction of Jayadhrata's laughter. The arrow struck Jayadhrata and he was killed.

Jayadhrata, king of Sindhu, was married to Dusshala, the Kauravas' sister.

The Fifth Fight, as Warriors

Drona accused Krishna of cheating. He ordered the Kauravas to continue fighting even after sunset, using lamps and torches to illuminate the battlefield.

Krishna told Ghatotkacha to lead the Pandava armies for, as son of Hidimbi, a rakshasa woman, he gained strength at night. To kill him, Karna was forced to use his most prized divine weapon, which would never miss its mark.

I am Bhima's son.

As I die, I will grow larger and fall on the Kaurava side, crushing my father's enemies to death.

Karna was known for his generosity.
Just before he had entered the battlefield, a
man had asked him for his divine armour
and earrings. Karna had given them to
the poor old man without a thought,
even though his armour and earrings
could save him from any weapon in
the world. The man had then revealed
to Karna that he was Indra, king of the gods.
He had taken Karna's protective armour
and earrings away as they would make him
more powerful than Arjuna on the battlefield.
But he had been so impressed by Karna's
generosity that he had given Karna a weapon that
would never miss its mark.

'I will use it against Arjuna,' Karna had said
with a smile. Unfortunately, he had no choice but
to use it against Ghatotkacha.

After being responsible for the deaths of Abhimanyu and Ghatotkacha, the fierce Drona went about killing Drupada and Virata. He seemed invincible, so Krishna came up with an elaborate plan to kill him.

Bhima, you kill an elephant called Ashwatthama.

Arjuna, you tell Drona that Ashwatthama is dead.

Drona will assume it is his son and he will look at Yudhishtira for confirmation.

80

The Boys Who Fought

Yudhishtira, say that indeed an Ashwatthama is dead, but you are not sure if it is a man or an elephant.

Nakula and Sahadeva, blow on your conch shells so that Drona does not hear Yudhishtira clearly and assumes the worst—that his son is dead.

In despair, Drona will stop fighting. As soon as he lowers his weapon, Dhrishtadyumna, you behead Drona.

Krishna's plan worked. Drona was beheaded. The Pandavas heaved a sigh of relief.

The Fifth Fight, as Warriors

Now Karna became commander of the Kaurava army. That's when Krishna told Karna the secret of his birth—that he was the eldest brother of the Pandavas. And that if he joined the Pandava side, he could stop the war and even become king. But Karna refused to desert Duryodhana.

> I choose friends over family. This is dharma.

> No, you choose the mighty over the meek. This is not dharma.

Kunti came to the battlefield at night and tried to get Karna to change his mind. He remained firm in his resolve. But out of the generosity of his heart, he made one allowance. 'I will not hurt any of your sons, mother of the Pandavas, except Arjuna!' he swore.

As luck would have it, during his fight with Arjuna, Karna's chariot got stuck in the mud. Even the magic formulas taught by his teacher did not work. He had to drop his bow and push the wheel out with his bare hands. While he was thus unarmed, and vulnerable, Arjuna shot him dead on Krishna's instructions.

I am Parashurama, Karna's teacher. Karna did not reveal his true identity to me, so I cursed him such that my lessons would fail him when he needed them the most. That is why he could not release the wheel from the earth using my mantras.

I am the earth. Once, when a girl spilt a pot of milk on me, Karna squeezed the milk out of me back into the pot, using his superhuman strength. To punish his irreverence, I squeezed the wheel of his chariot until he died.

Poor Karna, abandoned by his mother at birth, insulted by the Pandavas, exploited by the Kauravas, but generous to all while he lived, died pulling out a chariot's wheel, like a charioteer's son.

After Karna's death, when Shalya became commander of the Kaurava army, Yudhishtira impaled him with a spear, while Nakula and Sahadeva killed Shakuni using their swords.

Every day on the battlefield, Bhima had worked towards fulfilling his vow of killing each and every Kaurava by breaking their bones. He even washed Draupadi's hair with their blood so that she could finally tie it, having been worn loose for thirteen years.

Bhima ripped out the bowels of Dusshasana, the second Kaurava, who disrobed Draupadi.

After killing ninety-nine of his cousins, Bhima went about looking for Duryodhana, the hundredth Kaurava, and found him hiding inside a lake.
The two rushed towards each other, roaring like lions.
They fought long and hard.
Then Bhima, goaded by Krishna, surprised Duryodhana by striking his thigh. This was against the rules of warfare. But no one cared any more. The hundredth Kaurava howled in agony as he fell to the ground, unable to move, and slowly began bleeding to death.

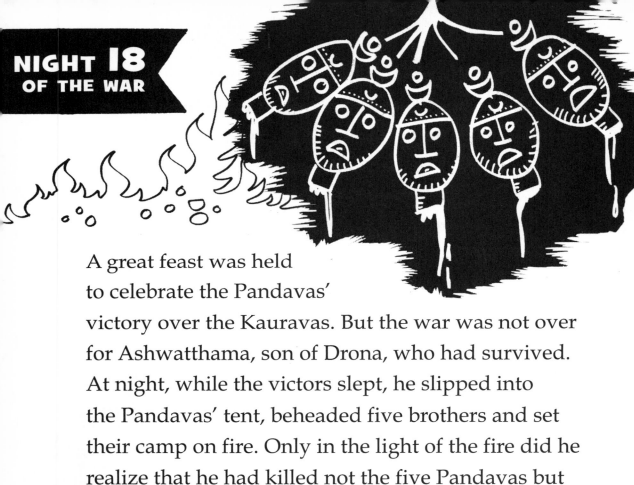

A great feast was held
to celebrate the Pandavas'
victory over the Kauravas. But the war was not over
for Ashwatthama, son of Drona, who had survived.
At night, while the victors slept, he slipped into
the Pandavas' tent, beheaded five brothers and set
their camp on fire. Only in the light of the fire did he
realize that he had killed not the five Pandavas but
Draupadi's five sons, the Upa-Pandavas.

> The Mahabharata is performed as Pandava Nritya in
> Uttarakhand and narrated as the Pandavani in Chhattisgarh.

The Boys Who Fought

Frustrated, Ashwatthama raised his bow and released a terrible arrow called the Brahma-astra towards the Pandavas. To counter it, Arjuna also released a Brahma-astra.

Krishna was alarmed, for the world would come to an end if the two weapons met each other. So he asked the two archers to pull the arrows back into their quivers. Arjuna could, but Ashwatthama couldn't. Instead, he redirected it towards the unborn child in the womb of Abhimanyu's widow, Uttari. This child was the only surviving heir of the Pandavas.

Krishna immediately shielded the baby and let the Brahma-astra strike his body instead. He then cursed the vengeful Ashwatthama. 'You will never die. Your wounds will never heal. You will spend eternity in pain and shame.'

Thus ended the war at Kuru-kshetra after eighteen days. All the Kauravas were dead. So were the children of the victorious Pandavas — Abhimanyu, Ghatotkacha and the five sons of Draupadi. The Pandavas even learnt that they had killed their own elder brother, Karna, whom they always called a charioteer's son. All because the Kauravas would not share a needlepoint of land.

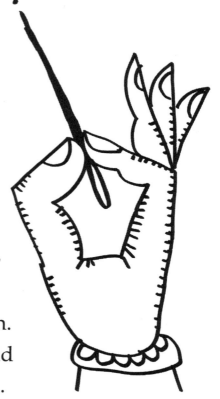

DID YOU KNOW? In folk versions of the Mahabharata, told in different languages in different parts of India, the other sons of the Pandavas died as well, including Iravan, son of Arjuna and the naga princess Ulupi, and Barbareek, grandson of Bhima, born of another naga princess.

The Boys Who Fought

The Sixth Fight, as Hermits

The war was over. The Pandavas had won.

The five brothers were invited to rule all the Kuru lands — not just the city of Indraprastha, but also the city of Hastinapur. But first, Pandu's sons decided to seek the blessings and the forgiveness of the elders.

When they went to meet Dhritarashtra, Krishna placed an iron statue between the blind king and Bhima. An angry Dhritarashtra hugged this statue and broke it in two, thinking it was Bhima, killer of his hundred sons. Later, he was relieved to learn that he had not actually killed Bhima.

Sailors spread the story of the Mahabharata from India to South-East Asian countries like Indonesia, Thailand and Cambodia.

The Boys Who Fought

Then they met Gandhari, who wanted to forgive them but could not control her anger. In fury, her eyes swelled up and, from the corner of her blindfold, she caught sight of Yudhishtira's toe, which was scorched by her rage and turned blue.

Gandhari then blamed Krishna for the war and cursed him. Krishna did not retaliate. He just hugged the mother of the Kauravas and comforted her.

In Tamil Nadu, some communities consider Draupadi and Gandhari to be goddesses.

The Pandavas then met Bhishma, who lay on his bed of arrows, waiting for a suitable moment to die. He gave the Pandavas detailed instructions as to how a king should uphold dharma. His teachings restored peace in Yudhishtira's heart.

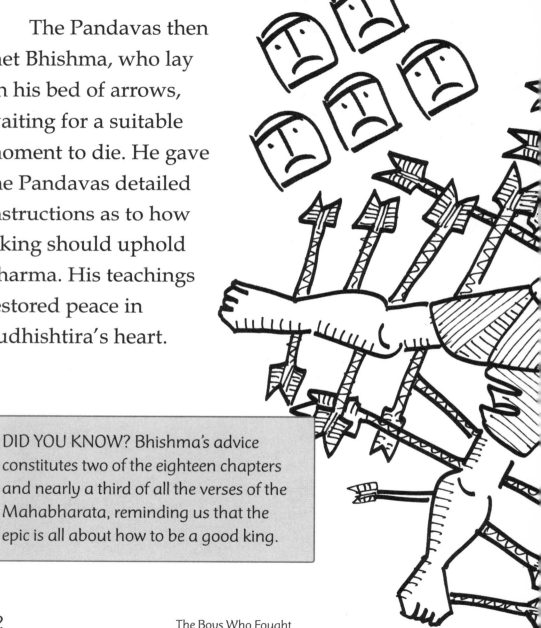

DID YOU KNOW? Bhishma's advice constitutes two of the eighteen chapters and nearly a third of all the verses of the Mahabharata, reminding us that the epic is all about how to be a good king.

After passing on his knowledge, Bhishma decided it was time to die, for the earth now had a good king.

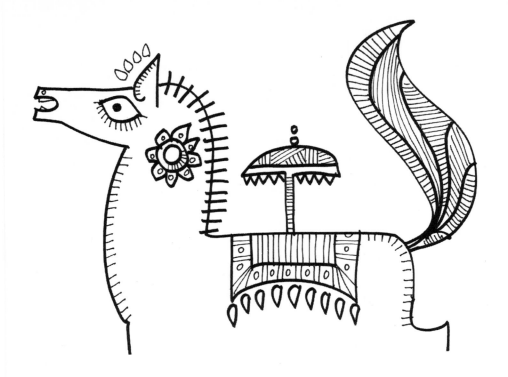

The Pandavas then returned to Hastinapur,
where Yudhishtira was finally crowned king. It was
a happy occasion after many years of sorrow.
The past was forgotten for it was a new beginning.
The royal horse of the Pandavas travelled all over
the world and, everywhere it went, spread the
message of peace and harmony.

The Boys Who Fought

When Abhimanyu's widow, Uttari, gave birth to his son, Parikshit, the elders of the family realized it was time for the old generation to retire. So Dhritarashtra and Gandhari decided to move to the forest. Kunti and Vidura accompanied them. They lived in the forest as hermits do, leading a simple life without palace luxuries.

Many years later, a forest fire claimed their lives. The elders did not resist for they no longer feared death.

DID YOU NOTICE? Letting go of things and desires is a common theme in the Mahabharata.

Meanwhile, far away, in Krishna's city of Dwaraka, a new war was brewing. The Yadavas who sided with the Pandavas argued with the Yadavas who sided with the Kauravas. Argument gave way to a brawl and a brawl turned into a fight. Not finding any weapons, the Yadavas struck each other with reeds that grew on the seashore. The reeds were so sharp that they served as weapons.

Krishna watched his family members kill each other before his eyes just as the Kuru elders had witnessed the Pandavas slaughter the Kauravas. Later, in the forest, a hunter mistook him for a deer and struck his foot with a poisoned arrow. Thus Krishna, cousin of the Pandavas, died like a beast of the forest.

Gandhari's curse had come true.

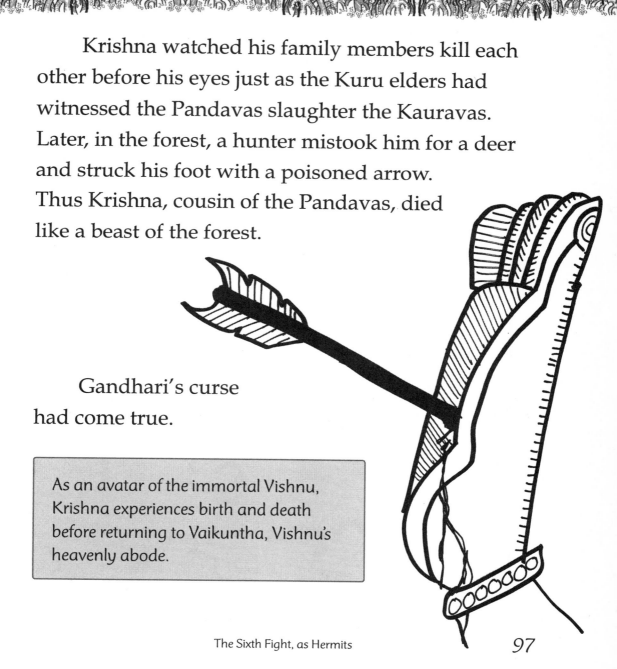

As an avatar of the immortal Vishnu, Krishna experiences birth and death before returning to Vaikuntha, Vishnu's heavenly abode.

The Pandavas ruled on earth until Parikshit grew old enough to become king. Then Yudhishtira passed on his crown and declared it was time for him to retire. He gave away all his wealth and bid everyone farewell. He left for the forest as a hermit, accompanied by his brothers and Draupadi. Barefoot, they walked north, towards the Himalayas.

The Mahabharata refers to two heavens: Swarga, where all desires are fulfilled, and Vaikuntha, where there are no desires.

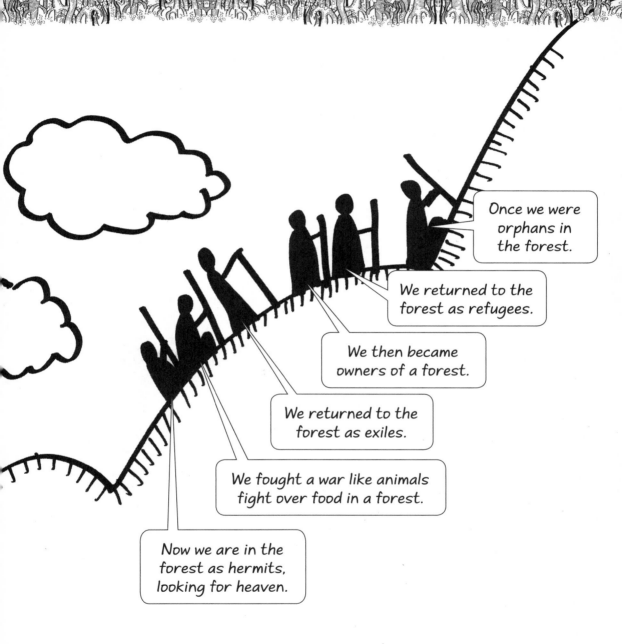

The Pandavas believed that since they had established dharma on earth, they would enter Swarga, the paradise of the gods, without experiencing death. However, as they climbed the mountains, one after the other, Draupadi and the Pandavas started slipping and falling to their deaths. Yudhishtira knew why. None of them were perfect.

Sahadeva was vain about his knowledge.

Draupadi did not love her five husbands equally.

Nakula was vain about his beauty.

Bhima was a glutton.

Arjuna was insecure.

Yudhishtira alone reached the gates of paradise.
A dog who had followed him from Hastinapur
accompanied him.

'You can enter but not the dog,' said the gods.

'That is not fair. I will not enter without this
faithful companion,' said Yudhishtira.

The gods were impressed. 'A fair king like
Yudhishtira deserves to enter Swarga without
experiencing death,' they said.

In Swarga, Yudhishtira saw Krishna. Then he also saw the Kauravas seated with the gods, enjoying the pleasures of paradise. He was not amused.

Where are my brothers and my wife?

They are suffering in a hell called Naraka.

Why? Did my brothers not establish dharma on earth along with me?

Did you not point out the imperfections of your brothers as they fell from the mountains?

Then why are the Kauravas here? They are more imperfect than my brothers.

You punished the Kauravas when you killed them at Kuru-kshetra. Have you still not forgiven them? How can heaven be yours if you are still angry?

The Boys Who Fought

But Yudhishtira was still upset.

The Kauravas did not share earth with you. You are not willing to share heaven with them. How are you different?

Yudhishtira then realized dharma is about fairness, not revenge. It is about sharing, not arguing. It is about love, not hatred. It is about forgiving, not fighting. And so he forgave the Kauravas!

In that instant, Swarga was filled with everyone he knew on earth: the Kauravas, the Pandavas, the Yadavas, Karna, Draupadi and the elders, even Shakuni and Vidura, all smiling and happy and at peace.

Conclusion
It's All about Sharing

Animals in the forest take food from nature.
Humans can give food to each other. When we
refuse to share food, the hungry attack and there
is war. Refusal to share led to the war between the
Kauravas and the Pandavas.

However, sharing
is not easy.

As orphans, the Pandavas suffered under the cruelty of their royal cousins. As refugees, they relied on the kindness of strangers. As kings, they realized how the same land cannot be home to humans and animals. As exiles, they learnt the value of generosity, tenderness, restraint and compassion from animals, birds and other forest creatures. As servants in the palace of Virata, they learnt how employers treat the poor and the powerless. As warriors, they learnt how to fight without hating and how rules do not matter if the intent is dishonourable. As hermits, they learnt to let go of all possessions. Still, despite victory in war, all the wisdom of the sages and the support of Krishna, the Pandavas found it difficult to share paradise with the Kauravas. They clung to hatred, like dogs clinging to bones, and found it hard to forgive.

It's All about Sharing

As long as we look for excuses, reasons and justifications to not share, the mighty will never take care of the meek and the meek will always hate the mighty. There will be no dharma in human society. If we have to fight, let us fight that urge within us that stops us from sharing, that urge that stops us from being human.

More from Devdutt Pattanaik

The Girl Who Chose
The Ramayana for Children

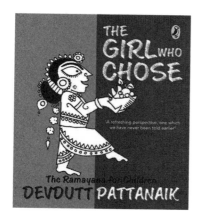

'You are bound by rules, but not I. I am free to choose.'

Over two thousand years ago, the poet-sage Valmiki wrote the Ramayana. It is the tale of Ram, the sun-prince of Ayodhya, who is obliged to follow family rules and so makes no choices. And of Ravana, king of Lanka, who does not respect anybody's rules or other people's choices.

Over the centuries, hundreds have retold the tale, in different languages, adding new twists and turns. But few have noticed that the tale always depends on the five choices made by Sita.

What were Sita's five choices?

India's favourite mythologist brings to you this charmingly illustrated retelling of the Ramayana that is sure to empower and entertain a new generation of readers.